CHRISTOPHER NORTON

MICROSWING

20 ORIGINAL PIECES BASED ON
SWING RHYTHMS FOR THE
BEGINNER TO INTERMEDIATE
PIANIST WITH PLAYALONG CD

BOOSEY & HAWKES

Boosey & Hawkes Music Publishers Ltd
www.boosey.com

Published by Boosey & Hawkes Music Publishers Ltd
Aldwych House
71–91 Aldwych
London
WC2B 4HN

www.boosey.com

© Copyright 2009 by Boosey & Hawkes Music Publishers Ltd

ISMN 979-0-060-12049-7
ISBN 978-0-85162-584-3

First impression 2009

Printed in England by The Halstan Printing Group, Amersham, Bucks

Piano: Christopher Norton
Tracks: Frank Mizen
CD Produced by Christopher Norton for CN Productions
Notesetting by Robin Hagues
Front cover design by Ian Middleton, Design United Ltd

www.christophernorton.com

CONTENTS

backing – track 1

performance – track 2

1. Top man

Christopher Norton

With pace, swung 8s ♩ = 132

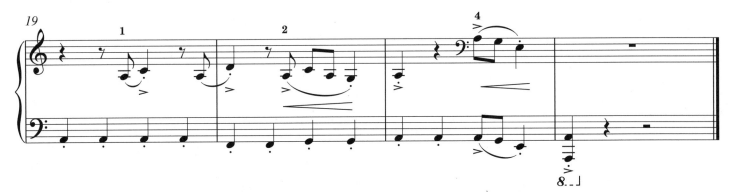

backing – track 3
performance – track 4

2. Irish swing

Christopher Norton

With pace, swung 8s ♩ = 120

backing – track 5
performance – track 6

3. Bits and pieces

Christopher Norton

Lightly, swung 8s ♩ = 120

backing – track 7

performance – track 8

4. All the way home

Christopher Norton

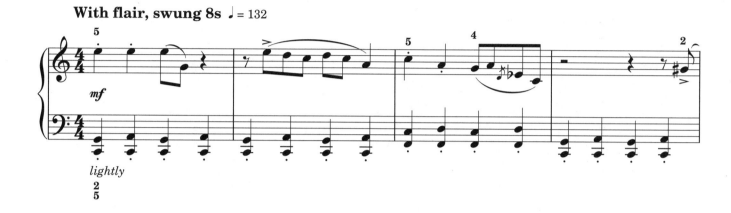

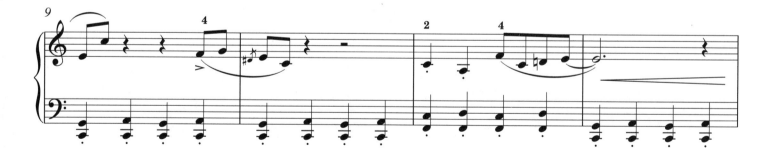

backing – track 9
performance – track 10

5. Five knights

Christopher Norton

Seriously, swung 8s ♩ = 138

con Ped

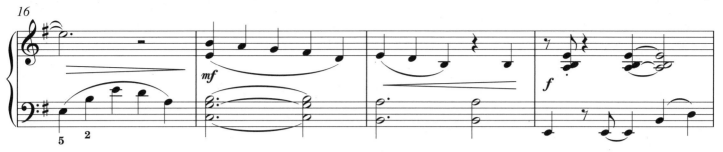

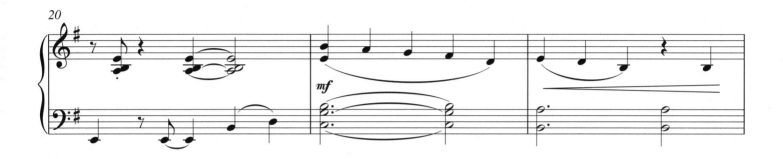

Slowing

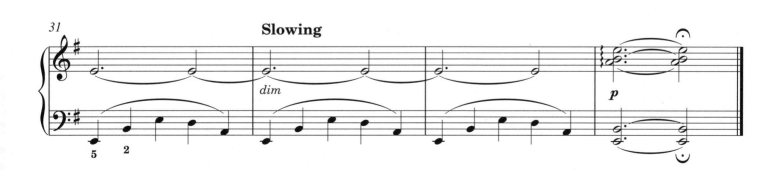

backing – track 11
performance – track 12

6. Township song

Christopher Norton

With pace, swung 8s ♩ = 152

backing – track 13
performance – track 14

7. Two-hander

Christopher Norton

Relaxed, swung 8s ♩ = 104

8. A simple tale

Christopher Norton

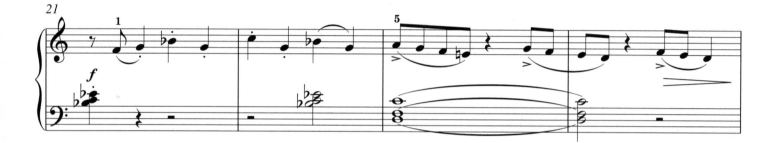

backing – track 17
performance – track 18

9. The spying game

Christopher Norton

Lyrically, swung 8s ♩. = 144

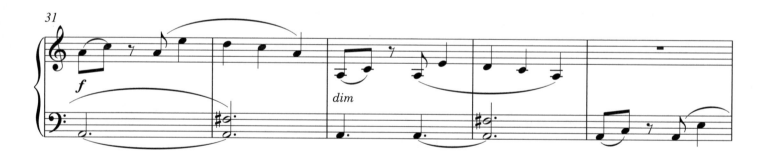

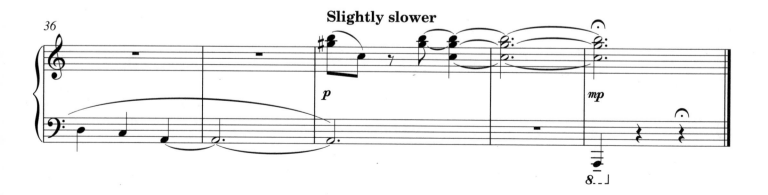

backing – track 19
performance – track 20

10. A happy occasion

Christopher Norton

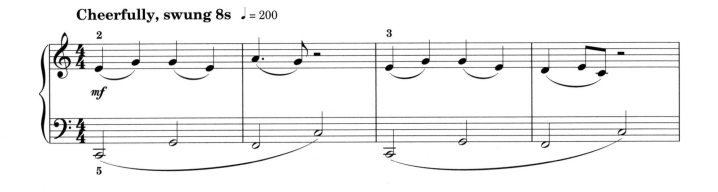

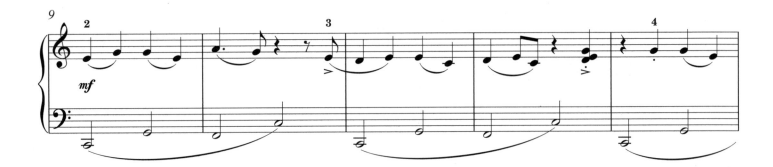

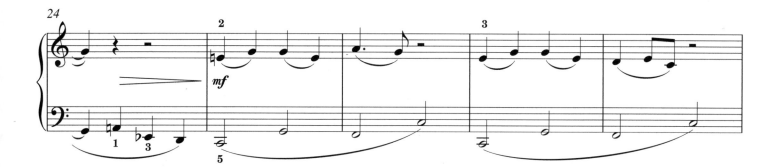

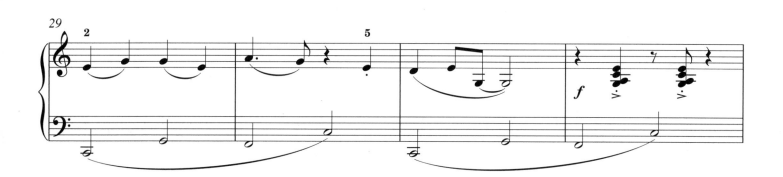

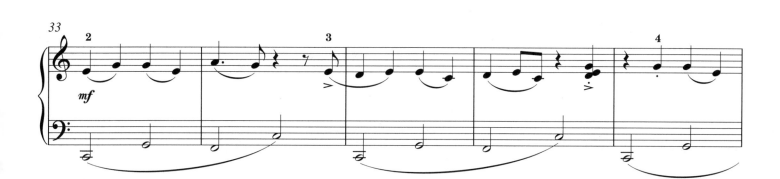

backing – track 21
performance – track 22

11. A little distracted

Christopher Norton

backing – track 23
performance – track 24

12. Played out

Christopher Norton

backing – track 25
performance – track 26

13. Casual air

Christopher Norton

Confidently, swung 8s ♩ = 126

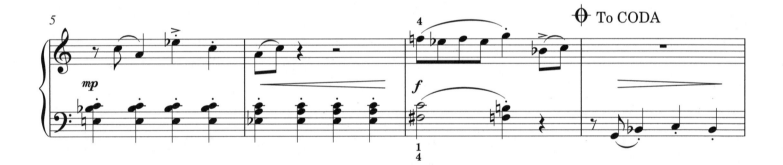

DC al ⊕ poi CODA

⊕ CODA

backing – track 27
performance – track 28

14. Today's the day

Christopher Norton

With quiet exultation, swung 8s ♩ = 112

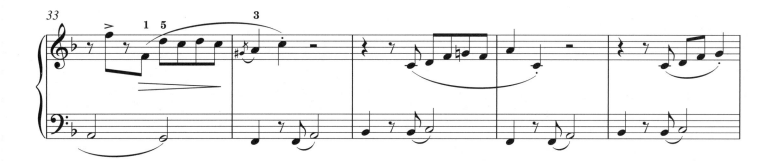

backing – track 29
performance – track 30

15. Prom night

Christopher Norton

backing – track 31
performance – track 32

16. Trail boss

Christopher Norton

Lively, swung 8s ♩ = 160

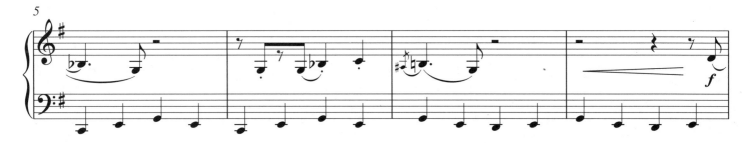

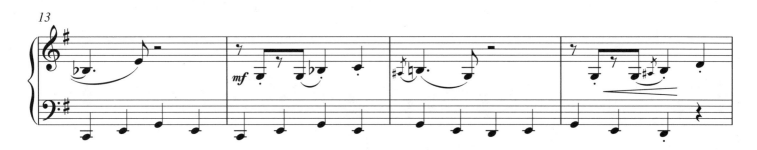

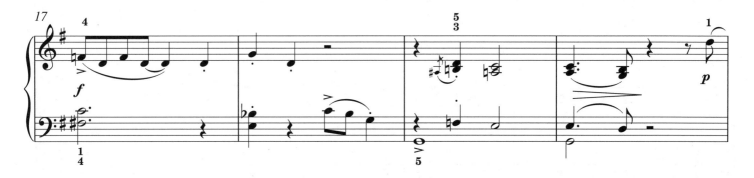

backing – track 33

performance – track 34

17. Guiding light

Christopher Norton

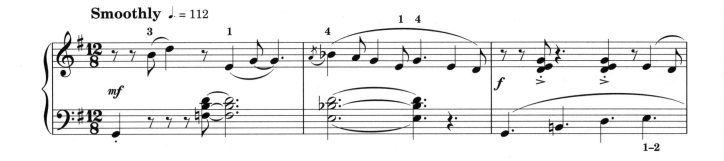

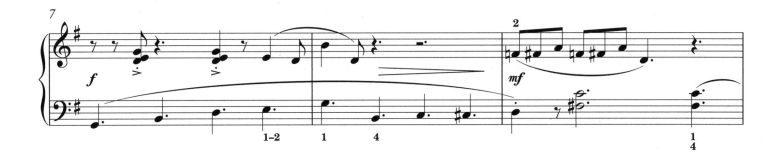

backing – track 35
performance – track 36

18. In the playground

Christopher Norton

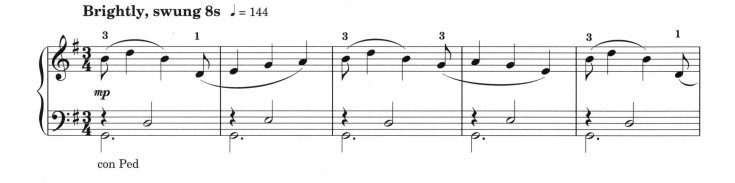

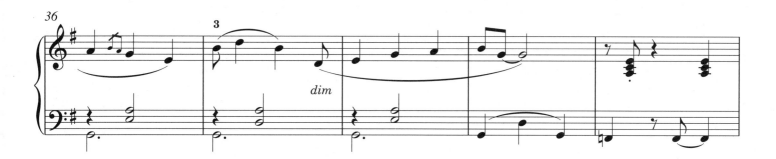

Slowing to the end

backing – track 37
performance – track 38

19. Early evening

Christopher Norton

Cool, swung 8s ♩ = 108

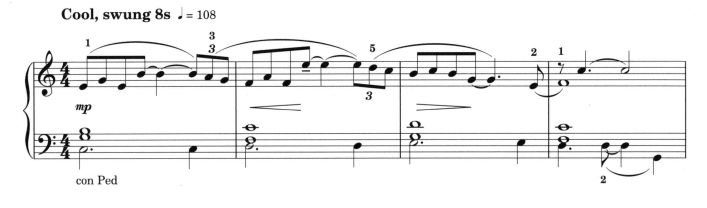

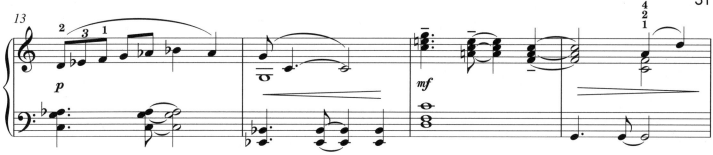

backing – track 39
performance – track 40

20. Blues lament

Christopher Norton

senza Ped

Slowing

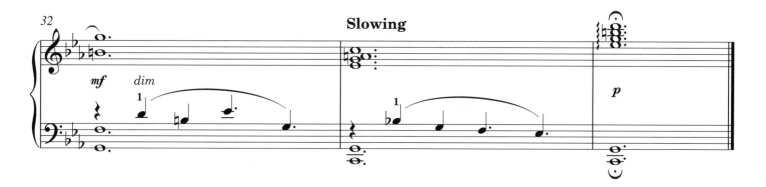